DESPICABLE ME 2™

THE OFFICIAL MINION MANUAL

Your Go-To Guide for ALL THINGS MINION!

By Howie Dewin

Based on the Motion Picture Screenplay
Written by Cinco Paul & Ken Daurio

SCHOLASTIC INC.

ISBN 978-0-545-54186-2

12 11 10 9 8 7 6 5 4 3 2 1   13 14 15 16 17 18 19/0

Printed in the U.S.A.   40
Designed by Joan Moloney
First printing, September 2013

THE OFFICIAL
MINION MANUAL

Jaleel

Contents

So you want to be a Minion. Or perhaps you want to get to know the Minions better. Or maybe you want to figure out what a Minion is and why everyone is talking about them.

Whatever the case, you've come to the right place. Here in this book, you will learn how to find your "Inner Minion."

So dive in. Find the Minion in you. Even if you can't achieve that perfect banana-yellow glow, you can still become a Minion by following the examples in this book!

In the name of mischief, mayhem, and ba-na-nas, GOOD LUCK!

Who Are the Minions?

The Minions are Gru's henchmen. They do whatever Gru needs them to do.

Gru is their hero. When Gru is happy, the Minions are happy. When Gru is sad, the Minions are sad.

Gru used to be a super villain, but now he's a dad. That means the Minions used to make explosives, but now they make jelly. They used to help steal famous landmarks. Now they babysit.

And one more thing: **Minions** ALWAYS **follow orders . . .**

. . . except when they get distracted, which is a LOT.

Minion Basics

Not all Minions are the same. Of course not! But they do share some basic characteristics that make them easy to spot.

Large eye or eyes. ("One eye or two?" is a common question in Minion circles.)

Stylish, silver, metal goggles suited to each Minion's number of eyes.

Overalls in a lovely denim blue. They are styled perfectly for the shoulder-challenged and for those who feel legs are less important than bodies.

Gru's logo. Because no self-respecting Minion would ever work for anyone else!

Key Words:

Yellow.
Pill-shaped.
One-eyed (or) two-eyed.
Great teeth.
Blue overalls.
Silver goggles.
Little.

But, you ask, how little? Well . . .

How Big is Little?

| Gru | Margo | Edith | Agnes | Unicorn |

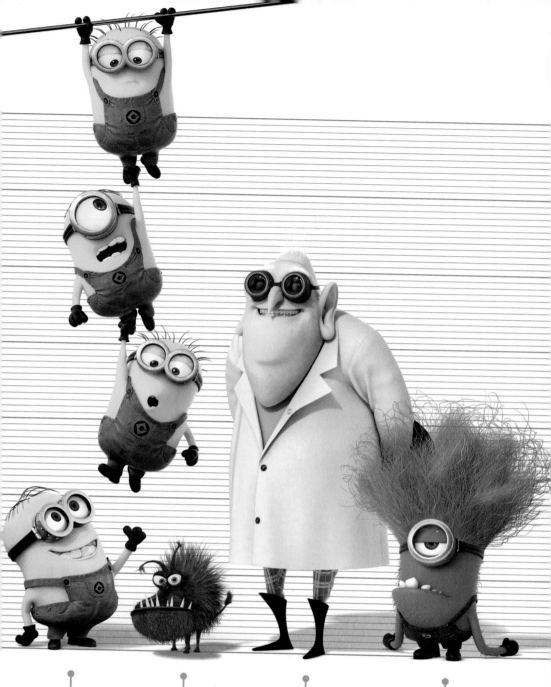

Minions　　**Kyle**　　**Dr. Nefario**　　**Evil Minion**

How to Talk Minion

The basic vocabulary you'll need to blend into any gathering of Minions.

Ba-na-na

A delicious yellow, crescent-shaped fruit worth getting blown up for

Bapple

A red, round fruit that's only worth chasing if there are no ba-na-nas

Eek

An expression of surprise when one realizes one might be blown up

Uh-oh

A troubled expression when one realizes he is, in fact, going to be blown up

Ow

An expression of pain when one is blown up

Bomba

The thing that blows up

Putt-Putt

A popular Minion amusement played with a long stick, small ball, and stylish hat with a pom-pom

Bello

A popular greeting in Minion circles

Poopaye

A popular farewell

Heh-heh-heh

An expression of amusement when not using "ha-ha-ha"

Ha-ha-ha

See "heh-heh-heh"

Evil Minion Speak:

Blaaarghhh.

Minions at Play

In some ways, Minions are no different than you or me.

They enjoy lullabies . . .

THE MINION LULLABY

Bo doo bleeb
Bo boo geep
Bo dwa dah do dah dwa maaa . . .
Bo doo bleeb maa
Bo boo geeeeeep
Bo do bleeb blob blah
blo maaa . . .

They play . . .

They dress up for Halloween . . .

They learn . . .

They do crazy stunts . . .

Knowing every Minion fact and figure doesn't mean a thing if you don't know this:

Yellow = Good. Purple = Evil!

This is what a good (and by good, we mean mischief-making, ba-na-na-stealing, and chaos-creating) Minion looks like.

This is what a good Minion + a dropper full of PX-41 looks like . . . a furry purple Minion of EVIL!

The Competitive Minion

One thing's for sure—Minions love games and sports.
And they want to beat one another . . .
no matter what!

Skateboarding!

Fishing!

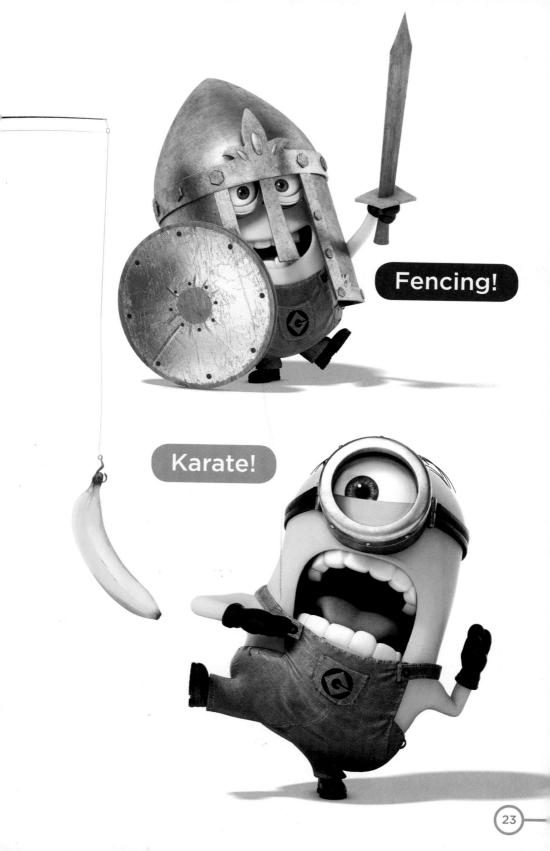

Fencing!

Karate!

Dance-Off!

Snorkeling!

Surfing!

Minions at Work

Minions are loyal to Gru, and they are very capable at lots of different jobs.

House Cleaning

Management

Research

Party Planning

27

Emergency Services

Top-Secret Undercover Work

Entertainment

Baking

R & R, Minion-Style

Do not be misled. Minions are not all about work. They **know** how to relax!

The Perfect Day

8:00 A.M.	Wake up
8:01 A.M.	Eat ba-na-nas
9:30 A.M.	Play games
10:45 A.M.	Ice-cream party
11:15 A.M.	Dance *Swan Lake*
Noon	Eat ba-na-nas
1:00 P.M.	Read favorite book (*Sleepy Kittens*)
1:30 P.M.	Nap
2:30 P.M.	Steal somebody's ba-na-nas. (Stolen ba-na-nas taste better.)
2:45 P.M.	Eat stolen ba-na-nas
3:00 P.M.	Beach time!
3:45 P.M.	Float in inner tube
4:30 P.M.	Build a rocket
5:15 P.M.	Blast off in just-made rocket
6:00 P.M.	Eat ba-na-nas
7:00 P.M.	DANCE!

Now that you truly understand the Minions, it's time to meet some of them! All you have to do is turn the page. . . .

Meet CARL

Name: Carl

One Eye or Two? One eye

Interesting Fact: Carl enjoys testing explosives—even if it means getting blown up every now and then.

Meet DAVE

Name: Dave

One Eye or Two? Two eyes

Interesting Fact #1: Thinks it's just good fun to shoot off rockets

Interesting Fact #2: Likes playing pretend

Meet JERRY

Name: Jerry

One Eye or Two? Two eyes

Interesting Fact: Fond of stuffed-crust pizza

Meet TOM

Name: Tom

One Eye or Two? Two eyes

Job: Cleans house

Interesting Fact #1: Often vacuums in a maid's uniform

Interesting Fact #2: Finds the name *Ramsbottom* extremely amusing

Meet PHIL

Name: Phil

One Eye or Two? Two eyes

Job: Undercover work, especially when it involves fake hair

Interesting Fact #1: Enjoys babysitting

Interesting Fact #2: Also enjoys karaoke

Meet STUART

Name: Stuart

One Eye or Two? One eye

Interesting Fact #1: Knows karate (or at least the poses)

Interesting Fact #2: Dave was Gru's first choice with the shrink-ray gun, but thanks to laser-fast reflexes, Gru got Stuart instead

Meet TIM

Name: Tim

One Eye or Two? Two eyes

Meet KEVIN

Name: Kevin

One Eye or Two? Two eyes

Interesting Fact: Enjoys golf and has one heck of a backswing

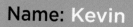

Meet The EVIL MINIONS

Name: The EVIL Minions!

Interesting Fact: The evil Minions eat metal like it's candy (or ba-na-nas).

A Minion's Guide to Babysitting

You'll never make it as one of Gru's Minions if you don't know how to keep the girls entertained when Gru puts you in charge! Here are some useful tips:

A clown nose improves most situations.

Plungers make great suction cups when hanging from the ceiling.

It's okay if the lab gets blown up as long as the girls don't!

In a pinch, toilet brushes make great unicorns.

Good-night kisses are always a good idea.

When creating the illusion that a large fairy is flying, don't let go of the rope.

When playing pretend, always remember: It's just a game. Also, explosives are not toys.

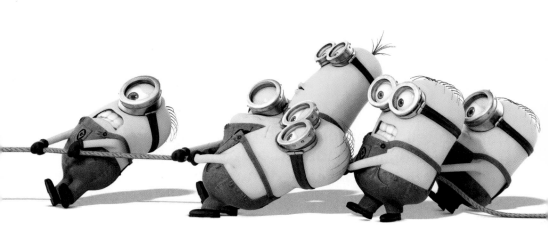

A tutu makes anything better.

SPOT QUIZ:
Innocent or Evil?

Can you tell the difference between a yellow Minion and a purple Minion, based only on the description below? Is the act described the work of a mischievous yellow Minion, or an evil purple Minion?

1 You are at school working hard on a book report. You go to the copy room and find a Minion sitting on the copy machine as it makes copy after copy of his backside. Two other Minions are rolling on the floor laughing. What are all three Minions?

2 You are waiting at a stoplight when you suddenly find your scooter being swallowed by a Minion. What is that Minion?

3 You return home after school to find a neat hole cut in your ceiling. Ropes and pulleys are dangling down into your kitchen, and all your ba-na-nas are missing. What Minions broke into your home?

4 You witness a Minion eating a child's tricycle. What is that Minion?

Turn to page 64 to check your answers!

Top Ten Ways to Become a Minion!

1. Never say no to a ba-na-na.

2. Always have a spare pair of blue overalls (with extremely tiny legs.)

3. Make sure your goggles have the same number of eyes as you do.

4. Never let another Minion beat you . . . at anything.

5. Always be ready for fun!

6. When making jam for Gru, try not to eat the merchandise.

7. Never miss a chance to create mayhem!

8. Work hard. Play harder.

9. Be yellow!

10. Above all else, be loving and loyal to your family.

Can You Pass the Minion Quiz?

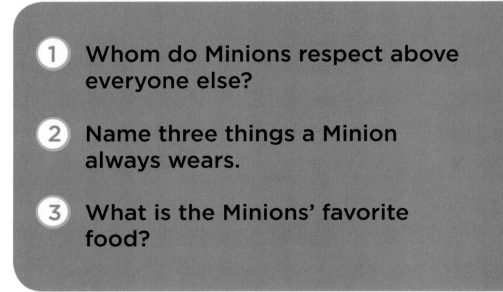

1. Whom do Minions respect above everyone else?

2. Name three things a Minion always wears.

3. What is the Minions' favorite food?

4 What is sewn on every Minion's uniform?

5 True or False: Minions hate the beach.

6 What products do the Minions make when Gru retires from being a supervillain?

7 How many fingers do Minion gloves have?

8 Which Minion enjoys vacuuming in a maid's uniform?

Turn to page 64 to check your answers!

Quiz Answers

Page 56-57:
1) yellow
2) purple
3) yellow
4) purple

Page 60-61:
1) Gru
2) overalls, goggles, and gloves
3) ba-na-nas
4) Gru's logo
5) false

Page 62:
6) jams and jellies
7) three
8) Tom